ACTION LAB ENTERTAINMENT PROUDLY PRESENTS

# Vamplets

## THIS BOOK IS BASED ON ORIGINAL CHARACTERS, STORY AND ART CREATED BY GAYLE MIDDLETON

### WRITTEN BY

## GAYLE MIDDLETON
### &
## DAVE DWONCH

### ART BY

## AMANDA CORONADO
### WITH
## BILL BLANKENSHIP

### EDITED BY: DARYL BANNER, JAY KAMHI AND BETH DOBIN-COLLAKU

BRYAN SEATON - PUBLISHER
KEVIN FREEMAN - PRESIDENT
SHAWN PRYOR - VP DIGITAL MEDIA
SHAWN GABBORIN - EDITOR IN CHIEF
DAVE DWONCH - CREATIVE DIRECTOR
JASON MARTIN - EDITOR
CHAD CICCONI - BASS PLAYER IN THE MUSICAL MAYHEM SOCIETY
COLLEEN BOYD - ASSOCIATE EDITOR
JAMAL IGLE - DIRECTOR OF MARKETING

# CHAPTER 1

"A MEETING WITH DESTINY"

I MEAN BEFORE YOU BECAME A *GUIDANCE COUNSELOR?*

LIKE, MAYBE YOU WANTED TO BE A FIREMAN...REALLY *SAVE LIVES.*

I *DO* SAVE LIVES, DESTINY HARPER.

HERE'S THE THING, I HAVE NO IDEA WHAT I WANT TO DO WITH MY LIFE.

I DON'T HAVE ANY SKILLS, I HAVE NO PROSPECTS, NO FRIENDS...

IT SAYS HERE THAT YOU'RE A SOLID 3.0 STUDENT.

CERTAINLY YOU HAVE *SOME SKILLS,* DESTINY.

I'M GOOD WITH KIDS. WELL, MY SISTER'S KID. IS BABYSITTING A SKILL?

FOR TEN DOLLARS AN HOUR, IT'S *A START.*

NOTHING EVER HAPPENS TO ME.

SCHOOL. WORK. REPEAT.

IT'S LIKE THE PERFECT RECIPE FOR BORING.

SIGH...

THANKFULLY, THERE'S THE *K AND P.*

I HIT ALL THE THRIFT STORES AND SHOPS AROUND TOWN, BUT KNIGHT AND PAWN IS THE BEST.

IT'S FILLED WITH ANTIQUES, MUSTY HATS, CLOTHES, KNICK KNACKS AND AN ASSORTMENT OF BIZARRE ODDITIES--

--STUFF THAT NO OTHER PAWN SHOP WOULD TAKE.

HELLO, DESTINY!

HEY, MRS. BLACKTHORNE.

HOW MANY TIMES DO I HAVE TO TELL YOU, GIRL, CALL ME *ANNIE*.

YES, MRS. BLACKTHORNE. ANY NEW ARRIVALS?

I SPEND HOURS IN THIS OLD PLACE. I LOVE IT HERE.

NOT MUCH, I'M AFRAID. A FEW NEW PIECES, NOTHING SPECIAL.

THERE ARE ALWAYS TREASURES TO BE FOUND.

THIS IS THE ONLY PLACE I FEEL *FREE*.

THIS PLACE IS *AMAZING!*

AND THAT'S WHEN I SEE IT.

"SEE" IS THE WRONG WORD.

MORE LIKE IT **CALLS** TO ME.

AS IF IT KNOWS THAT IT'S SUPPOSED TO BE MINE.

YOU ARE SUPPOSED TO BE MINE, AREN'T YOU?

HOW MUCH FOR THE LOCKET, ANNIE?

AND THE NIGHT JUST KEEPS GETTING WEIRDER.

Looking for adventure?
Thrills? Danger?
Seeking employment in
child care services?
Look no further!

The Nightcare Nursery
wants YOU!

No experience necessary.
inquire at
3370 Graves End Road.
This Sunday ONLY.

TAKING CARE OF BABIES AT NIGHT...*THAT* I CAN DO.

THANK YOU, WEIRD FLYING MOTH MAN!

UGH! GROSS!

I... I...

ZZZZZZZ

# CHAPTER 2

"THE TROUBLE WITH NANNIES"

THAT ONE... PENELOPE RANCID. WELL, I GUESS THINGS COULD BE WORSE.

IT'LL BE NICE TO HAVE A GIRLFRIEND, NO OFFENSE, RASKET.

WAIT, WHAT?! MY MASTER'S DEGREE IN TRANSLATION GUARANTEES I'LL BE PAIRED WITH A VAMPYRE...

...A YETI AT THE VERY LEAST!

NO WAY AM I GOING HOME WITH A TEENAGED MORTAL!

YOU SOUND LIKE... LIKE A *SNOB*.

CALL ME WHAT YOU WILL, BUT I'D NEVER HANG WITH SOMEONE LIKE *YOU*...

...ESPECIALLY IF I HAD, Y'KNOW, *LEGS*.

AND I THOUGHT YOUR *LOOKS* WERE GROSS!

YOUR ATTITUDE *STINKS*!

YOU WANT TO KNOW WHAT STINKS?

BEING ATTACHED TO A *MORTAL*.

YOU'RE LUCKY I HAVE STUDENT LOANS TO PAY, 'CAUSE *THIS* IS *GROSS*!

WHATEVER. LET'S GO SHOPPING.

PLEASE
LET ME BY.
I HAVE TO—

ooOFF!!

# CHAPTER 3

"PANDEMONIOUS DIRGE"

GAHHH!! HOW LONG HAVE YOU BEEN HERE?!

LONGER THAN I'D PREFER, MORTAL.

I'M AFRAID I MUST REPORT THAT MR. G IS, TO SAY THE LEAST, DISAPPOINTED IN YOU.

UH, IS THIS A DRAWING? IT LOOKS CUTE!

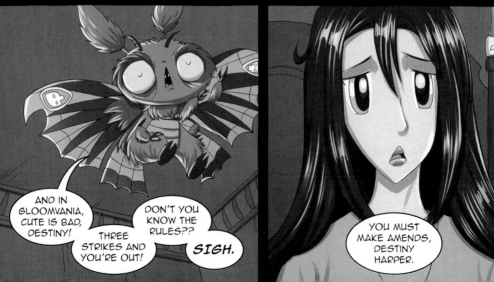

AND IN GLOOMVANIA, CUTE IS BAD, DESTINY!

DON'T YOU KNOW THE RULES??

THREE STRIKES AND YOU'RE OUT!

SIGH.

YOU MUST MAKE AMENDS, DESTINY HARPER.

AS YOU KNOW, THE VAMPLETS NEED BLOOD TO SURVIVE, BUT THERE IS A SEVERE SHORTAGE-

-SO MR. G IS SENDING YOU TO THE SOURCE.

THE SOURCE?

UNDEAD DRAGONS ARE THE SOURCE OF ALL THE BLOOD IN GLOOMVANIA.

YOU ARE BEING SENT TO THE *MILKING GROUNDS.*

I-I DON'T BELIEVE MILKING... DRAGONS... IS IN MY JOB DESCRIPTION, SIR.

YOU WILL BE FINE. UNDEAD DRAGONS ARE JUST LIKE--

--WHAT ARE THOSE THINGS ON EARTH?

*COWS.* THEY'RE LIKE COWS. ONLY HUGE, SCALY, *AND MEAN.*

BUT-

UP, UP, DESTINY!

NO "BUTS". MR. G'S PATIENCE IS WEARING THIN! YOU OFFENDED ALL THOSE POOR GLOOMVANIANS AT THE BIZARRE BAZAAR.

BUT-

OUT OF BED!

TODAY YOU REDEEM YOURSELF!

I ONLY JUST SET HIM DOWN. WHERE IS THE LITTLE—

—THERE.

HE'S A CLEVER LITTLE FUR BALL, ISN'T HE?

PERHAPS WE SHOULD JUST CATCH HIM, LYCINDA?

A WISE DECISION, STINKBUG. HIS PARENTS WILL WANT HIM *LIVING*, AFTER ALL.

MR. G WILL BE SIMPLY DELIGHTED TO HEAR EVEN MORE BAD NEWS, I'M SURE.

# CHAPTER

# 4

## "HOW TO MILK YOUR DRAGON"

SWEET LUCK!

I'M GOING TO NEED YOUR HELP ROARI. YOU TOO, LILY! ALL YOU HAVE TO DO IS SQUEEZE THE DRAGON WITH ALL YOUR MIGHT...

...JUST LIKE HUGGING RASKET! CAN YOU DO THAT FOR ME?

I FEEL SORRY FOR THE DRAGON ALREADY.

HEY! WAIT FOR ME!

HEY, GUYS!

UM... WHAT DID I MISS?

ALLOW ME. YOU, DESTINY HARPER, THROUGH SHEER INCOMPETENCE HAVE BEEN THE CAUSE OF THE FOLLOWING:

ONE, NEGLECT OF THE VAMPYRE BABIES CHARGED UNDER YOUR PROTECTION.

TWO, THE MISPLACEMENT OF ONE BABY WEREWOLF.

THREE, AND MOST DISTURBINGLY OF ALL, THE UNNEEDED TIDYING OF A PERFECTLY GRIM DOMICILE!

YES, YES...
I KNEW YOU WOULD
COME. AND OH, DO I EVER
HAVE NEWS FOR THE POOR,
YOUNG, MISFORTUNATE
DESTINY HARPER!

# CHAPTER 5

# "POTIONS, PREDICTIONS, AND PERIL"

OKAY, I THINK... I THINK I CAN DO THAT.

I THINK YOU'VE GOT IT! TO WIN BACK THE FAVOR OF THE VAMPYRE COMMUNITY, YOU MUST GIVE THEM WHAT THEY WANT! A SELFLESS ACT THAT SHOWCASES THE VERY WORST OF GLOOMVANIA! A CELEBRATION!

HAHA! ARE YOU ALWAYS SO UNSURE OF YOURSELF?

N-NO, I JUST~

YOU ARE STRONGER THAN YOU GIVE YOURSELF CREDIT FOR.

YOU MUST BELIEVE IN YOURSELF, OR NO ONE ELSE WILL, MORTAL.

AND NOW I LEAVE YOU WITH A WARNING. THERE ARE FORCES THAT WILL STOP AT NOTHING TO MAKE SURE YOU FAIL.

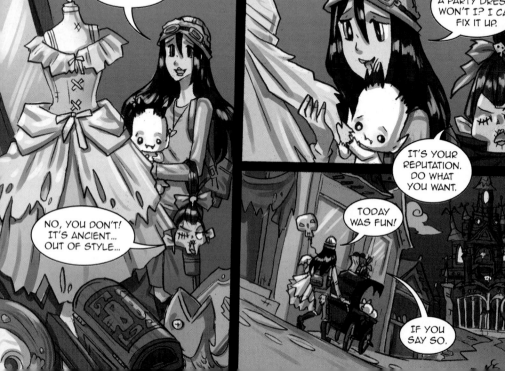

# CHAPTER 6

## "DANCE OF THE POISON BLACK MUSHROOM FAIRIES"